THE OFFICIAL GREENOCK MORTON QUIZ BOOK

THE OFFICIAL GREENOCK MORTON QUIZ BOOK

Compiled by
Chris Cowlin and Graeme Ross

Foreword by Douglas Rae

APEX PUBLISHING LTD

Hardback first published in 2009 by
Apex Publishing Ltd
PO Box 7086, Clacton on Sea, Essex, CO15 5WN, England
www.apexpublishing.co.uk

Copyright © 2009 by Chris Cowlin and Graeme Ross
The authors have asserted their moral rights

British Library Cataloguing-in-Publication Data
A catalogue record for this book
is available from the British Library

ISBN HARDBACK: 1-906358-31-1   978-1-906358-31-0

Typeset in 10.5pt Chianti Bdlt Win95BT

Cover Design: Siobhan Smith

Printed in Great Britain by the
MPG Books Group, Bodmin and King's Lynn

Author's Note:
Please can you contact me: **ChrisCowlin@btconnect.com** if you find any mistakes/errors in this book as I would like to put them right on any future reprints of this book. I would also like to hear from Greenock Morton fans who have enjoyed the test! For more information on me and my books please look at: **www.ChrisCowlin.com**

This book is an official product of Greenock Morton Football Club

We would like to dedicate this book to:

*All the players and staff who have worked for the
club during its history.*

FOREWORD

I am very pleased to have been asked to write the foreword for the new Greenock Morton Quiz book. Having been a supporter with a season ticket since I was 8 years old I have seen more players playing in the blue and white of Morton than 95% of our supporters.

The quiz book with some 800 questions will give much fun to supporters, young and old, at the many locations that Morton supporters meet. It will also be good to use when travelling to away matches in supporters' buses.

I personally look forward to studying the quiz book and brushing up on my knowledge and testing my memory recalling the players of yesteryear and even of lesser vintage.

If ever a publication was a 'must have' for Morton supporters, surely it must be 'The Official Greenock Morton Quiz Book'.

Hopefully you will spend many enjoyable hours studying the book and pitting your wits in battle with your friends and colleagues.

Best wishes

Douglas Rae, Greenock Morton Football Club (Chairman)

INTRODUCTION

I would first of all like to thank Douglas Rae for writing the foreword to this book. I am very grateful to him for his help and support on this project.

I would also like to thank everyone for their comments and reviews on this book (these can be found at the back of the book).

I would also like to thank Mary Davidson and Susan Gregory at Greenock Morton Football Club for their help during the book's compilation.

I hope you enjoy this book. Hopefully it should bring back some wonderful memories!

It was great working with Morton historian Graeme Ross. We have given you a selection of easy, medium and hard questions so it will be fun for all the family!

In closing, I would like to thank all my friends and family for encouraging me to complete this book.

Chris Cowlin .

Best wishes
Chris Cowlin

www.apexpublishing.co.uk

DAVIE IRONS

1. Davie became Morton manager in 2008. In which month?

2. Following on from the previous question, which team did Morton beat 2-1 at home to record Davie's first win as Morton manager?

3. What position did Davie guide Morton to in Division One in his first season in charge at Morton?

4. At which team was Davie player/manager between 1997 and 2002?

5. Which Scottish team did Davie manage before taking over at Cappielow Park?

6. What is Davie's middle name?

7. True or false: Davie won 10 under 21 international caps for Scotland?

8. Against which Premier League team did Davie guide Morton to a 4-3 away win during August 2008 in the League Cup?

9. In which year was Davie born – 1960, 1961 or 1962?

10. Which club did Davie play for between 1988 and 1991?

LEGEND – ANDY RITCHIE

11. In what year was Andy born?

12. In what year did Andy sign for Morton?

13. And can you remember Morton's opponents when Andy made his debut for Morton?

14. Against which team did Andy score his first Morton goal?

15. How many goals did Andy score in his first season with Morton – 17, 22, or 28?

16. In which year did Andy win the Scottish Football Writers' Player of the Year Award?

17. Against which English International goalkeeper did Andy score a hat-trick in 1979?

18. True or false: Andy never won a full Scotland cap?

19. Which team did Andy join from Morton?

20. Following on from the previous question, can you recall the Manager who signed Andy from Morton?

MORTON AND ST MIRREN - 1

21.   In which year did the teams first meet in the Scottish FA Cup – 1882, 1890 or 1898?

22.   True or false: Morton won both League matches against St Mirren during the club's first ever meeting in the Scottish League?

23.   Who played in goal for Morton when the sides met in the Scottish Challenge Cup semi-final during September 2005?

24.   True or false: Morton was unbeaten against St Mirren during their four League matches during 1999/2000?

25.   In April 1999 Morton beat St Mirren 5-1at Love Street. Which player scored a hat-trick?

26.   Following on from the previous question, which striker scored Morton's two other goals in the game?

27.   Can you name Morton's two scorers in the 2-0 home League win during April 1998?

28.   True or false: Apart from Renfrewshire Cup matches, the sides never met during the 1950s?

29.   Which Morton defender was sent-off during the 3-0 home League win during November 1997?

30.   Which striker scored Morton's equaliser in the 68th minute in the 1-1 away draw in the League during January 2000?

THE EARLY YEARS

31. In what year was Morton founded?

32. Who was the first Morton player to be capped by Scotland?

33. What was the name of Morton's first ground?

34. In which year did Morton win their first Renfrewshire Cup – 1892, 1893 or 1894?

35. In what year were Morton elected to the Scottish League?

36. In what year did Morton first move to Cappielow?

37. Which famous Scotland goalkeeper began his career with Morton as an outfield player?

38. Morton reached their first Scottish Cup semi-final in 1897. Who did they play and what was the score?

39. In what year did Morton first play in the Scottish First Division?

40. Morton again reached the semi-final of the Scottish Cup in 1904. Who were their opponents this time?

MORTON AND KILMARNOCK

41. In which round of the Scottish Cup did the sides meet in 2007?

42. Following on from the previous question, who scored a brace for Morton in the 3-1 win?

43. The sides first met during the 1895/1896 season, which team won both matches during that season?

44. What was the score when Morton beat Kilmarnock in the League Cup 2nd round during August 1993?

45. True or false: The clubs have met in every decade since the clubs first met in the 1895/1896 season?

46. Who finished higher in the League during 1988/1989 – Morton or Kilmarnock?

47. During the 1920/1921 season the sides were involved in an 11 goal thriller, what was the score during the Morton home game?

48. When Morton play Kilmarnock away at what stadium would they be playing?

49. True or false: Morton were unbeaten in their four matches against Kilmarnock during 1980/1981?

50. Which Morton midfielder scored a brace against Kilmarnock in the 5-2 home defeat in the Scottish Cup 5th round during March 1997?

MORTON MANAGERS

51. With which club did Tommy McLean begin his playing career?

52. In what year did Erik Sorensen become Morton manager – 1972, 1973 or 1974?

53. Who was Morton Manager the last time Morton reached a major cup semi-final?

54. Which Morton manager signed Mark McGhee for the club?

55. Who did John McCormack succeed as Morton manager?

56. Ally Maxwell won a Scottish Cup winners' medal with which club?

57. Which former Morton player had a temporary spell as manager in season 1983/84?

58. Who took over as manager from Allan McGraw?

59. Which former Morton boss won the European Cup as a player?

60. Who was the Morton manager when the club reached the 1948 Scottish Cup Final?

LEAGUE GOALSCORERS

*Match up the player with the amount of League goals
he scored in his Morton career*

61.	Mark McGhee	4
62.	Joe Caven	4
63.	Derek McInnes	50
64.	Jim Tolmie	3
65.	Marko Rajamaki	17
66.	John Goldthorp	19
67.	Dougie Robertson	19
68.	Jim Duffy	29
69.	John Boyd	37
70.	Hugh Strachan	36

LEGEND – ALLAN McGRAW

71.   In which city was Allan born?

72.   In what year did Allan join Morton – 1960, 1961 or
        1962?

73.   How many League and cup goals did Allan score in
        season 1963/64?

74.   Against which goalkeeper did Allan score a penalty in
        the 1963 League Cup semi-final replay?

75.   How many goals did Allan score in a 7-3 victory over
        Brechin City in 1963?

76.   Against which team did Allan score four goals in
        December 1964?

77.   In what year did Allan join Hibernian?

78.   In what year did Allan become Morton Manager –
        1984, 1985 or 1986?

79.   In what season did Allan manage Morton to the First
        Division Championship?

80.   Can you name the ex Hibs' player who was Allan's
        assistant in the 1980s?

JIM McINALLY

81.   In what year was Jim born – 1963, 1964 or 1965?

82.   True or false: Jim played for both Dundee clubs during his football career?

83.   Which two English clubs did Jim play for during his football career?

84.   How many Scotland caps did Jim win – 1, 10 or 30?

85.   In how many Scottish Cup Finals did Jim play?

86.   With which team did Jim begin his playing career?

87.   In what year did Jim become Morton Manager?

88.   Following on from the previous question, who did Jim replace as Morton Manager?

89.   Which Irish side did Jim manage for a short period?

90.   Jim resigned as Morton Manager after a home defeat against which side?

TON GOALIES

91. Which Scottish International goalkeeper played three games for Morton in 1986?

92. Which former Celtic and St Mirren goalkeeper was Morton's goalie in their first Premier League match?

93. Can you name the Morton goalie of the 1960s who shares the same name as an outfield player of the 1970s?

94. Who was the Morton goalkeeper when the team won the First Division championship in 1984?

95. Which goalkeeper played over 200 league games for both Morton and St Mirren and won a League cap for Scotland?

96. This Morton goalkeeper of the 1970s shares the name of a famous Scottish author. Can you name him?

97. In 1970 Morton had two Danish international goal keepers on their books, Erik Sorensen and...?

98. With which club did Paul Mathers begin his career?

99. This Morton goalkeeper won one Scotland cap against Wales. Who is he?

100. What nationality is Lee Robinson who was on loan to Morton in season 2007/08?

LEAGUE APPEARANCES

Match up the player with the amount of League appearances he made during his Morton career

101.	Jimmy Cowan	5
102.	Kai Johansen	194
103.	Bobby Adamson	179
104.	Murray McDermott	23
105.	Stan Seymour	3
106.	Jim Kiernan	67
107.	Barry Mitchell	141
108.	Chris Millar	26
109.	Jorn Sorenson	233
110.	Billy Sweeney	35

LEGEND – JOE HARPER

111. In what year was Joe born – 1947, 1948 or 1949?

112. How old was Joe when he made his Morton debut?

113. Following on from the previous question, in which competition did Joe make his competitive debut for Morton?

114. How many League goals did Joe score in season 1966/67 – 28, 29 or 30?

115. Which Yorkshire side did Joe join in 1967?

116. Following on from the previous question, can you recall the transfer fee?

117. Against which Glasgow side did Joe score a hat-trick at Cappielow in 1968?

118. In which year did Joe join Aberdeen?

119. True or false: Joe played in the 1978 World Cup Finals for Scotland?

120. For which Edinburgh side did Joe play in the 1970s?

LOAN PLAYERS

Can you recall which club loaned the player to Morton?

121. Ricky Sbragia

122. George Cowie

123. Paul Hartley

124. Ray Hudson

125. Graham Payne

126. Paddy Connolly

127. Kevin McDonald

128. Alex Reid

129. Mike Ring

130. Kenny Mitchell

BENNY'S BOYS

Can you name the players who played for Morton between 1976 and 1983 under Benny Rooney?

131. **Unsung midfielder of 1977/78 First Division champions' side who moved on to Airdrie.**

132. **Local boy who played for Aberdeen, Motherwell and Queen of the South before coming to Cappielow in 1978.**

133. **Livewire striker with dodgy perm who returned to Cappielow later in his career.**

134. **Signed from Alloa in 1978 as Mark McGhee's replacement.**

135. **A powerhouse midfielder who won two Scottish League caps.**

136. **Goalkeeper signed from Hong Kong Rangers.**

137. **Energetic midfielder signed from Queens Park.**

138. **Cult midfielder or striker signed from junior football.**

139. **Benny went back to one of his former clubs, St Johnstone to sign this striker who sadly, didn't live up to his name.**

140. **This midfielder was signed from Hamilton Accies, and was a squad player in Benny's First Division championship side.**

2008/2009

141. Which player scored Morton's first League goal of the season?

142. Can you name the two players who Morton signed from St Johnstone in July 2008?

143. True or false: Morton didn't win a League game in their first nine games of the season?

144. Which forward scored a brace in the 4-2 away win against Clyde during March 2009?

145. Which forward scored both goals for Morton in the 2-0 home win against Dundee during April 2009?

146. In which position did Morton finish in the League?

147. Who scored Morton's winning goal in the 2-1 home League win against Ross County during December 2008?

148. Which forward scored a brace in the 4-1 away win against Queen of the South during November 2008?

149. True or false: Morton drew their first four League games of 2009?

150. Which forward signed for Morton from Hamilton Accies initially on loan in October 2008 and then on a permanent basis during January 2009?

GREAT DANES

Morton has a history of signing Danish players.
Can you name these Great Danes?

151. This Dane returned to Morton to coach under Benny Rooney.

152. This Dane won five caps as a Morton player.

153. This Dane also played for Dundee and Kilmarnock.

154. This Dane won the Fairs Cities Cup shortly after leaving Morton.

155. This Danish centre half was transferred to Hibernian.

156. This Danish goalkeeper was signed from an American side.

157. This Dane was signed from an Italian side.

158. This Dane scored a hat-trick against Celtic in 1969.

159. This Dane was signed from a French club.

160. This Dane scored in a Scottish Cup Final.

STRIKERS

Can you recall these Morton strikers?

161. Signed from one half of the 'Old Firm' in 1991, this striker scored 31 League goals for Morton in two seasons and later played for Dundee United.

162. This English striker scored twice against St Mirren in a 3-0 victory in 1997.

163. This striker signed in 1969 from Shettleston Juniors.

164. Brother of a Dundee United and Scotland centre half who signed from East Fife and later returned to Bayview.

165. This local born striker played most of his football in England. He had two spells at Cappielow and is known as 'The Legend of Brunton Park'.

166. Considered to be one of Morton's greatest centre forwards, he scored over 100 goals for Morton in the 1920s after signing from Shawfield Juniors.

167. A local boy, this centre forward scored a hat-trick against Queens Park in Morton's run to the 1948 Scottish Cup Final.

168. This centre forward scored 72 goals in 101 games in just four seasons after signing from Clyde in 1951.

169. This striker scored a hat-trick in a 6-0 victory over Dundee United in 1969.

170. This 1950s centre forward scored 62 goals for Morton before moving across the Clyde.

1910-1919

171. What was the score when Ton defeated Rangers at Ibrox in 1910?

172. Following on from the previous question, which two ex Rangers players played for Morton in the game?

173. Which legendary English winger signed for Morton in 1912?

174. Following on from the previous question, which club did Morton sell the player to?

175. From which English side did Morton sign Jimmy Gourlay?

176. Following on from the previous question, which other local side did Jimmy play for in his career?

177. Which trophy did Morton win in 1915?

178. Morton achieved their highest ever (old) First Division League position in 1917. What was it?

179. What was the high score in a League match at Cappielow against Hibernian in 1919?

180. Which Morton player who signed for the club in 1916 was later inducted into the USA Soccer Hall of Fame?

WINNING GOALS

Can you recall the players who scored the winning goal for Morton in the following matches?

181. **Morton 1 Aberdeen 0 Premier League Cappielow January 1980.**

182. **Rangers 0 Morton 1 Premier League Ibrox 1981.**

183. **Morton 1 Celtic 0 Premier League Cappielow 1979.**

184. **Morton 1 Celtic 0 Premier League Cappielow 1978.**

185. **Dundee 0 Morton 1 Scottish First Division November 1971. This striker scored the only goal of the match on his debut.**

186. **Rangers 0 Morton 1 Scottish First Division Ibrox 1965.**

187. **A young full back, later to sign for one of the 'Old Firm' scored the winner in a 2-1 victory over Forfar in 1967.**

188. **Morton 1 Aberdeen 0 Premier League December 1980.**

189. **Dundee United 1 Morton 2 Tannadice 1978 Morton's first ever Premier League victory.**

190. **Morton 1 St Mirren 0 New Year's Day derby 1976.**

TON TRIVIA

191. Morton captain Stewart Greacen has a famous uncle. Can you name him?

192. Which two famous English footballers played for Morton during World War II?

193. Which famous Olympic athlete raced at Cappielow in the 1920s?

194. Which Morton player published a book called In Full Flood?

195. How many goals did Joe Jordan score for Morton?

196. What musical instrument was famously played at matches at Cappielow in the 1960s?

197. Can you name the former Morton captain whose son played for Aberdeen in a Scottish Cup Final?

198. Which Morton Manager appeared in an advert for bread?

199. Which player played 142 successive games for Morton between 1963 and 1966?

200. In 1971, which English international centre forward claimed that 'Morton were the dirtiest side he had ever played against'?

POSITIONS THEY PLAYED

Can you recall the positions the following players predominantly played in throughout their Morton careers?

201. Danny Ferguson

202. Archie McFeat

203. John Nelson

204. Tommy Coakley

205. Willie Fotheringham

206. Colin Liddell

207. Jimmy Mitchell

208. Andrew McPherson

209. Andy Crawford

210. Charlie Brown

LEGEND – DEREK COLLINS

211. In which year did Derek sign for Morton?

212. Which League were Morton playing in when Derek signed?

213. Against which side did Derek make his Morton debut?

214. Against which side did Derek score his first goal for Morton?

215. Which Manager signed Derek for Hibernian?

216. Which Glasgow side did Derek play for?

217. Derek also played abroad. Do you know in which country?

218. In which year did Derek return to Morton for his second spell as a player?

219. How many competitive goals (League, League Cup and Scottish Cup) did Derek score for Morton?

220. Who were Morton's opponents in Derek's first match as Morton Assistant Manager?

WHERE DID THEY COME FROM?

Can you recall which clubs Morton signed the following players from?

221. **Ally Scott**

222. **Billy Sweeney**

223. **Barney Jensen**

224. **Dave McCabe**

225. **Joe Caven**

226. **Borge Thorup**

227. **Paul Walker**

228. **Davie Cupples**

229. **Mark McGhee**

230. **Mark Pickering**

NICKNAMES

Can you identify these Ton players by their nicknames?

231. **Casper**

232. **Twinkle Toes**

233. **Batman and Robin**

234. **Goldie**

235. **Sugar**

236. **Smiler**

237. **The Legend**

238. **Badger**

239. **The Wee Barra**

240. **Danger Man**

DIVISION TWO CHAMPIONS – 2006/2007

241. Which team finished in second place, eight points behind Morton?

242. How many of Morton's 36 League games did they win – 23, 24 or 25?

243. Who finished Morton's top scorer with 15 League goals in 34 starts?

244. How many league goals did Morton score in total – 66, 76, or 86?

245. Which team did Derek Lilley join when he left Morton in January 2007?

246. Which forward signed for Morton on loan during this season, making 36 League appearances, scoring 11 goals?

247. Which team did Morton beat 9-1 at home in the League match during April 2007?

248. Following on from the previous question, how many goals did Peter Weatherson score in the game?

249. Which team did Morton beat 2-0 at home on the opening day of the season at Cappielow Park?

250. True or false: Morton were unbeaten in their first 11 League games of the season?

HAL'S HEROES

One of Morton's most fondly remembered sides is the 1963 record-breaking League Cup Final side. How much can you recall about Hal Stewart's Heroes?

251. Can you name the player who scored in the quarter final and semi-final of the 1963 League Cup?

252. Which team did Morton defeat in the semi-final of the League Cup in 1963?

253. Following on from the previous question, who scored the winning goal in the semi-final replay?

254. Can you recall the name of the barrel-chested Morton full back, initials J.B?

255. Four members of the League Cup final side also played for the same Lanarkshire club. Name the club and the players.

256. This unselfish centre forward was surprisingly left out of the cup final side.

257. To the nearest 5000 what was the official attendance in the final - 95,000, 100,000 or 105,000?

258. From which English side did Morton sign winger Jimmy Wilson?

259. With which club did Hugh Strachan later win the League Cup?

260. With which three words did Hal sign off in his Morton programme notes?

BIG WINS – 1

261. Can you name the two players who scored doubles when Morton defeated Rangers 5-1 at Ibrox in 1910?

262. Which Danish player scored a hat-trick in a 6-0 victory over Stirling Albion in 1967?

263. Which Highland League side did Morton beat 7-1 in the Scottish Cup in 2004?

264. Which player scored three of Morton's goals in a 4-0 home victory over St Johnstone in 1995?

265. Which side did Morton beat 6-0 in a League match in October 1971?

266. In 1963, Morton beat Brechin City 7-3 in a League match. What was the score the next time the sides met a few weeks later?

267. Following on from the previous question, how many goals did Allan McGraw score in the two matches?

268. Which two Morton players scored a brace in the 6-1 away win against Airdrie in Division Two during November 2003?

269. Which Danish player scored for Morton in a 7-2 victory against Cowdenbeath in the Scottish League Cup in 1972?

270. Who scored the only goal of the League Cup match against Celtic at Celtic Park in 1971?

1920s

271. In which year did Morton win the Scottish Cup?

272. Which Morton winger won two Scotland caps in 1921?

273. In which year was the infamous Cappielow riot?

274. In which round of the Scottish Cup were Morton eliminated the season after they won the trophy?

275. Can you name the 'perfect' referee who played for Morton in the 1920s?

276. Which round of the Scottish Cup did Morton reach in 1920?

277. Can you name the Morton Manager when they won the Scottish Cup?

278. Which Morton player of the 1920s played in the 1931 FA Cup Final?

279. Which Morton player of the 1920s was the first player ordered off in a Scottish Cup Final?

280. Who was Morton's stalwart full back of the 1920s who became a Morton director?

TON TRIVIA - 2

281. Which Morton defender was born on Christmas Day 1953?

282. Which player scored twice in the last match of the 1975/76 season when Morton defeated East Fife 3-0 to avoid relegation to the Second Division?

283. How many times did Morton beat Aberdeen in League matches in season 1979/80 when the Dons won the Premier League for the first time under Alex Ferguson?

284. Warren Hawke has played in an FA Cup Final. Which side did he play for and in which year?

285. What was the unusual score in a match against Queen of the South in 2002?

286. Can you name the Morton goalkeeper who is married to the famous Scottish female footballer Julie Fleeting?

287. Which team beat Morton 8-1 on Christmas day 1965?

288. Which Morton player of the 1980s scored Third Lanark's last ever goal in the Scottish League?

289. Which Morton player with the initials 'MM' was born in Argentina?

290. Which former Morton striker scored the goal that knocked Don Revie's famous Leeds side out of the FA Cup in 1974?

HISTORY

291.   What is Morton's record victory?

292.   What is Morton's record defeat?

293.   What was the aggregate attendance for the 1948
       Scottish Cup Final and replay between Morton and
       Rangers – 185,258 225,258 or 265,258?

294.   Which side did Morton play in their only season in
       European football?

295.   Which Danish player scored for Morton in their only
       season in European football?

296.   In 1970 what significant change did the club make to
       their playing kit?

297.   In total, how many seasons have Morton spent in the
       Scottish Premier League?

298.   And what is Morton's highest League finish in the
       Scottish Premier League?

299.   What is the record attendance for a match at
       Cappielow?

300.   What was significant about Morton's Scottish Cup tie
       against Dundee United in 1974?

POSITIONS IN THE LEAGUE – 1

Match up the season with the position the club finished in the League

301.	1989/1990	1st
302.	1988/1989	7th
303.	1987/1988	8th
304.	1986/1987	11th
305.	1985/1986	9th
306.	1984/1985	1st
307.	1983/1984	5th
308.	1982/1983	10th
309.	1981/1982	12th
310.	1980/1981	7th

MORTON AND ST MIRREN - 2

311. When was the last season that both clubs played in the same division?

312. What was the score in the first ever Renfrewshire Premier League derby match?

313. Which former Morton goalkeeper was briefly St Mirren Assistant Manager in the 1980s?

314. What was the score in the Ne'er day derby in 1977?

315. What was the unusual feature of this match?

316. Which former St Mirren midfielder won a Division One medal under Allan McGraw in 1987?

317. Three members of Morton's 1963 League Cup Final side also played for St Mirren. Name them.

318. This international defender played for both clubs in the 1990s.

319. What is Morton's record League win over St Mirren?

320. True or false: St Mirren knocked Morton out of the Scottish Cup three seasons in a row in the 1980s?

BENNY'S BOYS - 2

321. Which player scored the winning penalty in the penalty shoot out against Kilmarnock in the 1979 Scottish League Cup quarter final at Rugby Park?

322. In which year did George Anderson make his Morton debut – 1969, 1970, or 1971?

323. Against which team did Neil Orr score his only League goal for Morton?

324. Which team did Joe McLaughlin sign for in 1983?

325. Who was Morton's captain when Benny Rooney's Morton side won the First Division in 1978?

326. Who was Benny Rooney's Assistant at Cappielow during their five seasons in the Premier League?

327. How much did Benny pay Celtic for Jim Duffy?

328. Which Belgian side did Jim Tolmie join when he left Morton?

329. Which player scored twice in a 3-2 home victory over Aberdeen in September 1979?

330. Against which team did Andy Ritchie score a hat-trick in a Scottish Cup third round replay in 1978?

NATIONALITIES - 1

Match the player to his nationality

331.	Robert Earnshaw	Irish
332.	Dave Brcic	Austrian
333.	John Maisano	Danish
334.	Martin Naylor	Welsh
335.	Andre Boe	Australian
336.	Karim Boukraa	Cameroonian
337.	Finbarr Flood	Canadian
338.	Kenneth Skovdam	American
339.	Marcus Sukalia	French
340.	Mel Bottiglieri	English

WHO AM I? - 1

341.   I was born in Dingwall. I played full back and centre back and I was transferred to a Northern English club in 1974.

342.   I was a hard as nails defender who played for Morton for ten years in the 1960s and '70s. I scored for Morton in a Scottish Cup semi-final.

343.   I signed for Morton in 1994 from a local amateur side and later played in the SPL. I played as a midfielder or full back, and I am now an SFA Community coach.

344.   I am a man of many clubs, and I briefly ousted David Wylie as Morton goalkeeper when Billy Stark became Morton Manager.

345.   I played for Morton in the Premier League. I am the father of a famous Scottish internationalist. I was Manager of an Ayrshire club.

346.   I was a 1970s full back or midfielder with a rocket shot. I won a First Division medal in 1978 and then moved to St Johnstone.

347.   I was an effervescent, hard working midfielder who had two spells at Cappielow in the Premier League. I then moved on to Dumbarton and Queen of the South.

348.   I also had two spells at Cappielow. I played in the Premier League. I was a central defender and midfielder. I captained the club, and was forced to retire in 1994 through injury.

349.   I signed for Morton from Celtic during World War II, and I won two Scotland caps.

350.   I played over 350 matches for Morton and was a member of the 1922 Scottish Cup winners' side. I later managed the club.

SCOTTISH CUP - 1922

351.   Who did Morton defeat in the semi-final of the 1922 Scottish Cup?

352.   What was the score?

353.   Which Morton star missed the final through injury?

354.   Which player replaced the above player?

355.   What was the official attendance in the final? (To the nearest 1000.)

356.   Name Morton's opponents in the final.

357.   Who scored the only goal of the final?

358.   What was notable about the goal?

359.   Who was the Morton goalkeeper in the final?

360.   Can you name the Morton captain in the final?

MORTON LEGENDS

361. Which shirt number did Bobby Thomson wear through out his Morton career?

362. In what year did Erik Sorensen sign for Morton?

363. From which team did Morton sign Rowan Alexander?

364. Which defender scored nine League goals when Morton won the First Division in 1977/78?

365. What age was Davie Hayes when he made his Morton debut in 1970?

366. How many goals did Janne Lindberg score in his Morton career – 5, 7, or 11?

367. True or false: Benny Rooney played six League matches for Morton?

368. Which team did Jim Holmes sign for when he left Morton?

369. How many Scotland under 21 caps did Neil Orr win?

370. In which city was Hal Stewart born?

CAPPIELOW CRACKERS

371. Which player had a goal disallowed in the final seconds of a match against Celtic in 1964 to deny Morton a famous 4-3 victory over Celtic?

372. Which player scored all four goals in a 4-0 win over Hamilton in 1977?

373. Morton and Hearts served up an eight goal Cappielow cracker in 1977. What was the final score?

374. Which side did Morton beat at Cappielow in 1978 to win promotion to the Premier League for the first time?

375. Following on from the previous question, can you name Morton's goal scorers in the match?

376. What was the final score in a Cup match against Aberdeen at Cappielow in 1996?

377. How many goals did Dean Windass score in the above match?

378. Which player scored a hat-trick for Morton in a 4-3 victory over Motherwell in 1974?

379. Which youngster scored his first two goals for Morton in a 6-0 thrashing of Motherwell in 1979?

380. Which player scored twice for Morton in a 5-2 victory over Kilmarnock in the Scottish League Cup in 1978?

2005/2006

381. Who was Morton's manager during this season?

382. In which position did Morton finish in Division Two?

383. How many of the club's 36 League games did they win – 20, 21 or 22?

384. Who finished Morton's top scorer with 12 League goals in 30 starts and three substitute appearances?

385. Which goalkeeper played in 29 of Morton's 36 League matches during the season?

386. Which player signed for Morton from Livingston in August 2005?

387. Which team beat Morton 1-0 on aggregate in the play-off semi-finals at the end of the season?

388. Which team did Morton beat 2-0 at Cappielow Park on Boxing Day 2005?

389. True or false: Morton were unbeaten during their four League matches during January 2006?

390. Which team did Morton beat 5-2 at Cappielow Park during September 2005?

TON TRANSFERS

391. Which two Lisbon Lions joined Morton in 1971?

392. How much did Morton receive when Mark McGhee moved to Newcastle?

393. Who was the Danish player who was transferred to Newcastle in 1969?

394. How much did Morton pay Berwick Rangers for Warren Hawke?

395. What is the record transfer fee received by Morton?

396. And what is the record transfer fee paid by Morton?

397. Which club did Neil Orr join in 1982?

398. Which Celtic player did Morton sign as a replacement for Neil Orr?

399. Which Port Glasgow born striker joined Morton in 1973 from Preston North End?

400. Which club did Neil McNab join when he left Morton?

WHERE DID THEY GO?

Can you recall which clubs signed these players when they left Morton?

401. Morris Stevenson

402. Matt Maley

403. John Goldthorp

404. John Anderson

405. Roddie Hutchison

406. Robbie Henderson

407. Scott McArthur

408. Peter Cormack

409. Scott Bannerman

410. Billy Osborne

LEGEND – BILLY STEEL

411. Where was Billy born?

412. And in which year?

413. Which club did Morton sign Billy from?

414. Against which country did Billy win his first cap?

415. How many full Scotland caps did Billy win as a Morton player?

416. What honour did Billy achieve as a Morton player in May 1947?

417. Billy moved to Derby County in June 1947. What was significant about the transfer fee?

418. True or false: Billy was the first Scotland player to be ordered off in a Scotland match?

419. Which other Scottish club did Billy play for?

420. How many caps did Billy win for Scotland?

JOHN McNEIL

421. From which Boys Club did John join Morton?

422. Can you remember John's nickname??

423. What age was John when he made his first team debut?

424. Against which team did John score his first goal for Morton?

425. Against which Premier League side did John score a superb goal in a Scottish Cup quarter final replay in 1978?

426. Which club did John join on loan in 1982?

427. To the nearest five, how many career goals (League, League cup and Scottish Cup) did John score for Morton?

428. Which club provided the opposition for John's testimonial match in 1990?

429. John named his best ever Morton 11 in his testimonial programme. Who did he choose as his goalkeeper?

430. How many seasons in total did John play for Morton?

1930s

431.   Name the Morton winger who was capped in 1930 against Wales.

432.   Which team did Morton defeat 11-2 in season 1935-36?

433.   Which player scored eight goals in the above match?

434.   Which long serving full back joined Morton from Morton Juniors in 1936?

435.   Which legendary Scottish Manager's brother played for Morton in the 1930s?

436.   Which former Morton winger resigned as Morton Manager in 1931?

437.   Which Morton player of the 1920s and 1930s won an FA Cup winners' medal with Arsenal?

438.   In which year did Morton lose to Aberdeen in the Scottish Cup semi-final?

439.   How many League goals did Morton score in season 1935/36 – 97, 117, or 127?

440.   How many goals did John Calder score in League and cup matches in season 1935/36?

MATCH THE YEAR - 1

441. Bobby Collins signed for Morton and Neil Armstrong walked on the moon.

442. Benny Rooney came to Cappielow and there was a heat wave summer.

443. Sean Connery starred in Goldfinger and Morton won the Second Division.

444. Joe Jordan signed for Leeds United and General Charles de Gaulle died.

445. Oasis released their debut album and Morton signed two Finnish players.

446. Billy Stark was appointed Morton Manager and the blockbuster movie Titanic was released.

447. Hal Stewart came to Cappielow and the Berlin Wall was constructed.

448. Elvis died and Morton thrashed Alex Ferguson's St Mirren 3-0 at Cappielow.

449. Jim Holmes and Rowan Alexander played for Scotland in a four Nations tournament and Coventry won the FA Cup.

450. Morton lost in a Scottish Cup quarter final replay and the world witnessed the fall of the Berlin Wall.

NAME THE YEAR

451.   Two Morton players played for a European select in Stanley Matthews testimonial, and for a bonus can you also name the players?

452.   Morton played in Europe for the only time.

453.   Morton lost to Queen of the South, ending a 27 match unbeaten record.

454.   Jim Duffy won the Scottish Footballer of the Year Award.

455.   Morton lost 7-1 in a Scottish League Cup semi-final.

456.   Jimmy Cowan won his final cap.

457.   Morton knocked Clyde out of the Scottish Cup and the Scottish League Cup.

458.   Morton topped the Premier League just before Christmas.

459.   Morton, with three teenagers in the side, (George Anderson, Davie Hayes and Joe Jordan) defeated Rangers 2-0 at Ibrox.

460.   Morton lost to Hamilton in the B&Q Cup Final.

NATIONALITIES - 2

Match up the player to his nationality

461.	Stan Seymour	Canadian
462.	Artur Correia	English
463.	Paul Fenwick	Irish
464.	Parfait Medou-Otye	English
465.	Jani Uotinen	Australian
466.	Paddy Turner	English
467.	Martin Foster	Finnish
468.	Lars Christensen	French
469.	Erik Paartalu	Danish
470.	Sean O'Connor	Angolan

1940s

471. Which final did Morton reach in 1942?

472. Cappielow was closed for a short spell in 1949. Where did Morton play their home matches during this time?

473. Which team did Morton play in the 1948 Scottish Cup Final?

474. Who scored Morton's goal in the 1948 Scottish Cup Final?

475. Which team did Morton defeat in the 1948 Scottish Cup semi-final?

476. And who scored the winning goal?

477. Neil Mochan was absent from the Morton side from 1946 to 1948, for what reason?

478. Which player scored a hat-trick in the Scottish Cup third round against Queens Park in 1948?

479. This winger moved to Michael Parkinson's home town club in 1945. Name the player and the club.

480. What was the nickname of Morton's popular full back of the 1940s, Andy Fyfe?

MORTON AND PARTICK THISTLE

481. What was the score when the sides met in the League during December 2008?

482. Which Morton player scored a hat-trick in the 4-2 home win against The Jags in the Division One match during October 2007?

483. Which defender scored the only goal in Morton's 1-0 League win during October 1996?

484. How many times did the teams meet during 1979/1980?

485. Following on from the previous question – how many times did Morton beat Partick in season 1979/80?

486. The teams were involved in an eight goal thriller during Morton's home match of the 1895/1896 season, what was the score – 5-3, 6-2 or 7-1?

487. True or false: Morton were unbeaten in their four matches in Division One against The Jags during 2007/2008?

488. Which team were formed first – The Ton or The Jags?

489. When Morton visit The Jags at which stadium are they playing?

490. Which Morton player scored the club's winning goal in the 79th minute in the 2-1 win at home during December 2005?

CAPPIELOW CAPTAINS

491. Who was Morton's captain in the 1948 Scottish Cup Final?

492. This player also played for St Mirren and Dundee United and captained Morton in the 1960s.

493. This player captained Morton in the 1970s, began his career with Celtic, and moved to an English club in 1972.

494. This player was capped for Scotland as a Celtic player and captained Morton in a Cup semi-final in the 1960s.

495. Who was the captain of the 1963 League Cup Final side?

496. This defender won three First Division Champions' medals with Morton and captained the club in the 1980s.

497. Who was Morton's first captain in the Premier League?

498. This player was one of Morton's youngest ever captains. He later played for Rangers and Scotland, and is now a successful manager.

499. This captain played for Morton in all Four Divisions of the Scottish League.

500. This midfielder captained Morton in the 1980s before he signed for an English club managed by a Lisbon Lion.

POSITIONS IN THE LEAGUE – 2

Match up the season with the position the club finished in the League

501.	1999/2000	6th
502.	1998/1999	11th
503.	1997/1998	1st
504.	1996/1997	5th
505.	1995/1996	9th
506.	1994/1995	7th
507.	1993/1994	8th
508.	1992/1993	8th
509.	1991/1992	3rd
510.	1990/1991	6th

STRANGE BUT TRUE

511. Which Morton goalkeeper later played for both Celtic and Rangers?

512. Which Morton player later became a professional sprint runner?

513. Which player played an unsuccessful trial match for Morton in 1963 and later scored for Scotland against England?

514. In the late 1960s Morton transferred four players to the same London club. Can you name the club and the players?

515. Can you name the player who scored an own goal when playing for Rangers against Morton in 1972, and later played for Morton in the Premier League?

516. Morton played Coventry City twice in 1965 in challenge matches. Who was the Coventry Manager?

517. Which player scored a hat-trick of penalties against Morton in 1973?

518. Which player was given a free transfer by Morton in 1983 and was later picked for the Republic of Ireland's World Cup squad?

519. Three players who had played for Scotland in the 1958 World Cup played for Morton in the 1962/63 season. Name them.

520. Can you name the Greenock born former Morton player who captained the USA team that defeated England in the 1950 World Cup?

ROY BAINES

521. Where was Roy born?

522. Following on from the previous question, in which year?

523. Which club did Morton sign Roy from in 1972?

524. In what year did Roy sign for Celtic?

525. To the nearest ten, how many games (League, League Cup and Scottish Cup) did Roy play for Morton in his two spells at the club?

526. Who was the Morton goalkeeper when Roy signed for Morton in 1972?

527. Roy's first competitive match against Stranraer had an unhappy outcome for Roy. What was it?

528. In his second spell at Morton Roy played in how many matches in a row? Was it 122, 182 or 222?

529. In what year did Roy return to Morton for his second spell?

530. Which club did Roy sign for in 1983?

LEGEND – JIMMY COWAN

531.   In what year was Jimmy born?

532.   In what year was Jimmy inducted into Scottish Football's Hall of Fame?

533.   In what year did Jimmy sign for Morton?

534.   Against which side did Jimmy make his Morton League debut?

535.   Against which country did Jimmy win his first full cap?

536.   In which year was the famous 'Cowan's Wembley'?

537.   How many full Scotland caps did Jimmy win?

538.   In 1951 Jimmy saved a penalty against Celtic. Which future Morton star took it?

539.   How many times did Jimmy play in a winning Scotland team against England?

540.   With which club did Jimmy finish his career in 1956?

JIM HUNTER

541.   In what year was Jim born?

542.   Which amateur side did Morton sign Jim from?

543.   Against which team did Jim make his Morton debut?

544.   And in what year?

545.   How many League matches from a possible 44 did Jim play in the 1986/87 season when Morton won the First Division?

546.   Jim formed a strong partnership with which whole-hearted centre half, who came to Morton from Aberdeen?

547.   In what season did Jim play his last match for Morton?

548.   In total, how many League matches did Jim play for Morton? (To the nearest ten.)

549.   How many goals did Jim score in his Morton career?

550.   Which famous English Manager once expressed an interest in buying Jim from Morton?

1950s

551.   Which future Morton player scored a hat-trick of penalties for Celtic in 1953?

552.   Which member of Morton's 1948 Cup final side was transferred to Aberdeen in 1952?

553.   Which English side did Neil Mochan transfer to in 1951?

554.   And do you know the transfer fee involved for the above?

555.   The nephew of a Morton great who helped Ton win the Scottish Cup in 1922 played for Morton in the 1950s. Can you name him?

556.   Which future Manchester City Manager played 44 games for Morton in the 1950s?

557.   How many goals did Neil Mochan score in a 4-3 victory over Celtic in season 1950/51?

558.   Morton was relegated to the Second Division in 1952. How many seasons did they subsequently spend there until they were promoted back to the First Division?

559.   Which striker scored 97 goals for Morton in only four seasons in the 1950s only to be rewarded with a free transfer?

560.   Can you name the high scoring winger who was transferred to Sunderland in 1955?

AWAY GAMES

*Can you name the team that Morton would be playing if
they were visiting the following stadiums in an away match?*

561. **Strathclyde Homes Stadium**

562. **Ochilview Park**

563. **Stair Park**

564. **Gayfield Park**

565. **Borough Briggs**

566. **Central Park**

567. **Galabank**

568. **Links Park**

569. **Victoria Park**

570. **Station Park**

LEGEND – BILLY CAMPBELL

571. In what year was Billy born?

572. Which junior team did Billy play for?

573. In which year did Billy sign for Morton?

574. Billy played for Scotland against England in 1943. What was the score in this match?

575. Billy's middle name is the same as both a knife and a musician. What is it?

576. How many official caps did Billy win for Scotland?

577. Which other Morton player played alongside Billy against Belgium in 1948?

578. What unusual circumstance prevented Billy playing against France in 1948?

579. In what year did Billy play his last match for Morton?

580. At which ground was Billy's testimonial played?

2004/2005

581. Who started the season as Morton manager?

582. In which position did Morton finish in the League?

583. From which team did Morton sign Chris Templeman during December 2004?

584. Can you name the two Morton players who scored 10 League goals during the season, to finish the club's joint top League scorers?

585. Can you name the only player to play in all 36 League matches during this season?

586. Which team did Morton beat 6-1 away from home during September 2004 with Peter Weatherson and Jason Walker both scoring braces in the game?

587. Which Morton midfielder scored a brace in the 4-2 home win on the last day of the season against Berwick Rangers?

588. Which team knocked Morton out of the Scottish Cup in 2005?

589. Which player signed from Livingston during March 2005?

590. How many of Morton's 36 League games did they win – 17, 18 or 19?

LEGEND – TOMMY ORR

591.   In what year was Tommy born?

592.   How old was Tommy when he signed for Morton?

593.   In which country did Tommy serve in the army in
       World War II?

594.   Tommy signed for Morton from which team?

595.   How many Scotland caps did Tommy win?

596.   And how many goals did Tommy score for Scotland?

597.   In which year did Tommy retire from football?

598.   To the nearest 10, how many competitive goals did
       Tommy score for Morton?

599.   In which year did Tommy's son, Neil make his Morton
       debut?

600.   Neil Orr played for three other Scottish teams. Can you
       name them?

BIG WINS - 2

601. Which players scored Morton's goals when they defeated Wolves 2-1 in the Texaco Cup in 1970?

602. Which player scored a hat-trick in a 5-0 victory over East Fife in 1978?

603. What was the score in the Renfrewshire derby at Love Street in September 1995?

604. Can you name all the Morton scorers in the 9-1 victory over Forfar in 2007?

605. What was the score in a League match at Cappielow against Stenhousemuir in 1966?

606. Who scored four goals for Morton in the above match?

607. Which Danish player scored a hat-trick in a 5-2 victory against Dundee United in 1968?

608. Which team did Morton beat 6-0 in the Scottish Cup in 1981?

609. Morton and Cowdenbeath shared 12 goals in a League match in season 1935/36. What was the score?

610. Which player scored four goals in a 5-1 victory over Brechin City in 1986?

1960s

611.   In which position did Morton finish in 1961 in the old Second Division?

612.   Which former Dundee and Scotland player was Morton player/coach for a spell in the 1960s?

613.   How many League goals did Morton score in season 1963/64?

614.   Morton played Chelsea in two challenge matches in 1962. Who was the Chelsea Manager?

615.   True or false: Sir Alex Ferguson's brother played for Morton in the 1960s?

616.   Which famous Scottish international winger played one friendly match for Morton in the 1960s?

617.   Which team knocked Morton out of the Scottish Cup in 1968 and at which stage of the competition?

618.   Morton won their first 23 League matches in a row in season 1963/64. How many goals did they score in this unbeaten run?

619.   In which League position did Morton finish to qualify for their only season in European competition?

620.   Which future England Manager played against Morton in a friendly in 1962?

DEREK LILLEY

621. In what year was Derek born?

622. From which Boys Club did Derek sign for Morton?

623. How many League goals did Derek score in his first season at Cappielow – 3, 13, or 23?

624. Against which side did Derek score two penalties at in a match at Cappielow in 1995?

625. Derek was Morton's top League goal scorer for three seasons in a row in the mid 1990s. How many League goals did he score in these three seasons - 40, 45, or 48?

626. Who was the Leeds United manager who signed Derek in 1997?

627. Which Scottish side did Derek join on loan in 1998?

628. In his two spells at Cappielow, how many goals did Derek score in League, League Cup and Scottish Cup matches? (To the nearest five.)

629. With which team did Derek win the Scottish League Cup?

630. Which Angus side did Derek join in 2008?

1970s

631. Which Greenock born former Hearts player coached Morton in the 1970s?

632. Which World Cup goalkeeper first played against Morton in 1962 and played his last ever match as a professional against Morton at Cappielow in 1979?

633. Which Danish player scored against Aberdeen with a wonder volley in a League Cup match at Cappielow in 1974?

634. In what year did Benny Rooney become Morton Manager?

635. Where was '70s striker Donnie Gillies born?

636. Which World Cup winner was Manager of Preston North End when they played Morton in the Anglo Scottish Cup in 1979?

637. What age was Bobby Collins when he played his last match for Morton?

638. Which 1970s Morton centre forward's brother played for Scotland in the 1986 World Cup?

639. Which Russian team played Morton in a challenge match at Cappielow in 1972?

640. Which former Celtic player scored for Morton in a 2-1 victory over Rangers at Ibrox in 1972?

2003/2004

641. Who was Morton's manager during this season?

642. In which position did Morton finish in the League –
      third, fourth or fifth?

643. Can you name both players who finished the club's top
      League scorers, both scoring 15 goals?

644. Which team did Morton beat 3-1 at Cappielow Park on
      the opening day of the League season?

645. Which team did Morton beat 6-4 at home during
      December 2003?

646. Which player scored a brace in the 5-2 home win
      against Stenhousemuir during October 2003?

647. True or false: Morton lost their last four League
      matches of the season?

648. With which team did Morton share a 3-3 away draw
      during February 2004?

649. Who scored Morton's equaliser in the 52nd minute at
      Cappielow Park against Hamilton Accies in the 1-1
      home draw during September 2003?

650. True or false: Morton were unbeaten in their six
      League matches during March 2004?

LEGEND - DAVID WYLIE

651. From which side did David sign for Morton?

652. Against which team did David make his Morton debut?

653. What was David's nickname at Morton?

654. How many League games did David play for Morton - 382, 482, or 582?

655. To the nearest ten, how many games did David play for Morton in all competitions?

656. Which team provided the opposition in David's testimonial match?

657. David is on record as stating that he considers his best save to be in a match against Ayr. Who was the player later to become Morton Manager, who David made the save from?

658. Which club did David join when he left Morton?

659. In season 1988/89 David played in all 39 League games for Morton. How many shut outs did he have?

660. Against which team did David play his last game for Morton?

JOE MASON

661.   In what year was Joe born?

662.   Which club was Joe's first senior club?

663.   What major honour did Joe win in the 1964/65 season?

664.   Joe signed for Morton in 1966. Which player moved to Kilmarnock as part of the deal?

665.   What was Joe's nickname at Morton?

666.   Morton knocked Kilmarnock out of the Scottish League Cup in 1967. How many goals did Joe score over the two legs?

667.   How many League and cup goals did Joe score in his first season (1966/67) with Morton?

668.   How many goals did Joe score in a League match against Alloa Athletic in 1967?

669.   In what year was Joe transferred to Rangers?

670.   Can you recall the transfer fee?

1980s

671.   Which player scored both Morton goals in a 7-2 home League defeat against Celtic in 1984?

672.   Which side did Morton lose 6-0 to, only to beat the same side the next time they played?

673.   Who replaced Benny Rooney as Morton Manager?

674.   Which ex Motherwell and Scotland striker's goals helped Morton to promotion to the Premier League in 1984?

675.   Which Morton striker of the 1980s has a son who plays with Dundee United?

676.   How many times were Morton relegated from the Premier League in the 1980s?

677.   Dundee United won all four Premier League matches against Morton in season 1984/1985. How many goals did United score in the four games?

678.   Who was Morton's top League goal scorer when they won the First Division in 1984?

679.   Which two players were ever presents in season 1981/82?

680.   Can you name the future Morton Manager who played for Scotland in the 1982 World Cup?

DIVISION THREE CHAMPIONS - 2002/2003

681.   Which team finished in second place in the League, one point behind Morton?

682.   How many of the club's 36 League matches did they win – 21, 22 or 23?

683.   Who scored the only goal of the title deciding match at Cappielow against Peterhead?

684.   Which player did Morton sign on a free transfer from Crystal Palace during August 2002?

685.   Which team did Morton beat 5-1 at home, in only their second League game of the season?

686.   True or false: Morton won their last five League matches of the season?

687.   Which team did Morton beat 5-0 at Cappielow Park during April 2003?

688.   Following on from the previous question, who scored a brace in the game?

689.   Which forward scored both goals in the 2-2 home draw against Stirling Albion in the League match during March 2003?

690.   Which player scored his first goal for the club in 1-1 draw with Queens Park in November 2002?

EXPERT - HISTORY

691.   Which side defeated Morton in the 1964 Scottish
        League Cup semi-final?

692.   How many times have Morton won the Renfrewshire
        Cup? (Until 2008)

693.   Which Yorkshire side did Morton play in the Texaco
        Cup in the 1970s?

694.   When was the first international match played at
        Cappielow?

695.   In which year was the present main stand at Cappielow
        opened?

696.   In 1988 Morton defeated Rangers in a League match
        at Cappielow. How many years had it been since their
        previous home League victory over Rangers?

697.   Morton lost only one League match in season 1963/64.
        Which side beat them?

698.   Who were Morton's first opponents in the inaugural
        Texaco Cup?

699.   Which player had a goal disallowed against Aberdeen
        in the 1979 Scottish League Cup semi-final?

700.   Six Morton Managers have been capped for Scotland.
        How many can you name?

DEBUTS

How much can you recall about these debuts?

701. Which centre half made his debut in Morton's first ever home Premier League victory?

702. This bustling centre forward scored twice on his debut against Airdrie in 1969.

703. Which forward destined for bigger things made his Morton debut against Raith Rovers in 1969?

704. Which team did Morton play when Derek McInnes made his Morton debut?

705. In what year and against which side did Chris Millar make his Morton debut?

706. In what year and against which side did Jim McAlister make his debut?

707. Which youngster made his Morton debut in 1971 aged 15 against Celtic at Parkhead?

708. Which local boy made his debut aged 15 against Partick Thistle in 1973?

709. Can you recall the score in the above match?

710. Against which team did Dominic Shimmin make his Morton debut?

EXPERT - ANDY RITCHIE

711.   How many competitive goals (League, League Cup and Scottish Cup) did Andy score for Morton?

712.   Andy won one Scottish League Cap. Who were the opposition?

713.   Which other Morton player played in the above match?

714.   Following on from the previous question, how many goals did Andy score in the match?

715.   Andy supported Motherwell as a boy. Can you remember the name of the ex Motherwell striker who Andy teamed up with at Morton?

716.   At which end of Cappielow did Andy score his memorable goal against Aberdeen in the 1981 Scottish Cup?

717.   Which team did Andy briefly manage in the 1980s?

718.   In Morton's first season in the Premier League, Andy scored direct from a corner kick. Against which team?

719.   How many times did Andy score a hat-trick against Dundee United?

720.   To the nearest five, how many Premier League goals did Andy Ritchie score for Morton?

2001/2002

721. Who started the season as club manager?

722. Can you name the goalkeeper who played in 33 of Morton's 36 League matches during this season?

723. Which forward signed from Queen of the South during November 2001?

724. Which team did Morton beat 4-1 at home on the opening day of the season with Scott Bannerman scoring a brace in the game?

725. How many of Morton's 36 League matches did they win – five, six or seven?

726. Which forward scored a brace in the 4-1 away win during November 2001 against Stranraer?

727. Which forward signed for Morton from Pollok Juniors in March 2002?

728. Who finished the club's top scorer with eight goals in 31 matches?

729. In which position did Morton finish in the League?

730. Who took over as manager of Morton in March 2002 and was eventually manager until November 2002?

1990s

731. How many times did Morton meet Celtic in the Scottish Cup in the 1990s?

732. Which former Morton player scored twice for Scotland against Estonia in 1997?

733. Against which side and in what year did Warren Hawke score his first Morton goals?

734. Which Morton player scored the only goal of the match when Morton beat St Mirren at Love Street in January 1996?

735. Which Morton player was sent off in the famous 5-1 victory over St Mirren at Love Street in April 1999?

736. Which club did Rowan Alexander join as Player/Manager when he left Morton?

737. Can you name the locally born Morton central defender who also played in midfield who played over 200 matches for Morton in the 1990s scoring 36 goals?

738. In which season did Morton win the Second Division championship?

739. Following on from the previous question, how many points did Morton win when they won the Second Division in 1994/95?

740. Which Morton player was Second Division Player of the Year in 1995?

MORTON AND THE 'OLD FIRM'

741. Two members of Morton's 1922 Scottish Cup Final side were transferred to Rangers. Can you name them?

742. Which member of the Rangers side that defeated Morton in the 1963 League Cup Final had two spells at Morton?

743. How many times have Morton beaten Rangers in the Premier League?

744. And how many times have Morton beaten Celtic in the Premier League?

745. Can you recall the Morton full back who moved to Celtic in 1968?

746. Which player scored both Morton's goals in a 2-1 victory against Celtic in 1984?

747. Can you name the three Danish players who Morton sold to Rangers in the 1960s?

748. Who scored Morton's goals when they beat Celtic 4-2 at Parkhead in 1969?

749. Which player had a goal disallowed against Rangers in the 1981 Scottish Cup semi-final?

750. Can you recall Morton's scorers when they defeated Rangers 3-2 at Cappielow in 1988?

EXPERT - JOE HARPER

751. True or false: Joe scored a hat-trick in a cup final and finished on the losing side?

752. Which side did Joe play for in the above match?

753. How many matches in a row did Joe score for Morton in season 1968/69?

754. When Joe left Aberdeen in 1981, he briefly managed which Highland League side?

755. Do you know the transfer fee Morton received from Aberdeen for Joe?

756. Against which country did Joe make his international debut?

757. And who was the Scotland Manager who chose him?

758. How many Scotland caps did Joe win?

759. And how many goals did Joe score for Scotland?

760. Joe played alongside which Morton player in the Scottish League side against the Irish League in 1969?

2000/2001

761. Which team did Morton beat 2-0 at home during August 2000, the club's first League win of the season in their third match of the season?

762. Who took over from Allan Evans as manager at the end of January 2001?

763. In which position did Morton finish in the League – 8th, 9th or 10th?

764. Which Morton forward scored the only goal in the 1-0 away win against Raith Rovers during September 2000?

765. Who scored a brace for Morton against Falkirk in the 3-1 away win during March 2001?

766. True or false: Morton's first League game of 2001 ended in a 6-0 home defeat?

767. Which Morton midfielder finished the club's top scorer with nine League goals?

768. Which team did Morton beat 3-0 away on the last day of the League season?

769. Which defender did Morton sign from Ross County during March 2001?

770. How many of the club's 36 League games did they win – seven, eight or nine?

EXPERT - ALLAN McGRAW

771. Which Northern Irish side did Allan play for?

772. Which organisation honoured Allan in 1997 with a tribute dinner?

773. One of Allan's first signings as Morton Manager scored 26 goals in his first season at the club. Name him

774. How many hat-tricks did Allan score in season 1963/64?

775. In which year did Allan's son Mark make his Morton debut?

776. For how many years was Allan Morton Manager?

777. Who was the former Aberdeen player who Allan brought to Morton as player/coach?

778. In which year did Allan sign Janne Lindberg and Marko Rajamaki?

779. Who was runner-up to Allan as Morton's top goal scorer in the 1963/64 season?

780. In 1963 Allan scored in all of Morton's first eight League matches. How many goals did he score in these eight games?

2007/2008

781. In which position did Morton finish in Division One?

782. How many of Morton's 36 League games did they win
      – 9, 11 or 13?

783. Which team did Morton beat 3-2 on the opening day
      of the League season?

784. Can you name the three Morton scorers who scored in
      the 3-0 home win against Dunfermline Athletic during
      April 2008?

785. Which team did Morton beat 2-1 away with Ryan
      Harding and Ryan McGuffie scoring the goals on 2nd
      January 2008, the club's first win of 2008?

786. Who was the only Morton player who played in every
      League game during this season?

787. Following on from the previous question, how many
      League goals did he score during this season?

788. Which forward signed from Celtic in August 2007,
      made 10 League appearances for the club and then
      signed for Ross County in January 2008?

789. Which player scored eight goals in 24 appearances plus
      six as substitute?

790. Which player finished the club's highest League scorer
      with nine goals in 33 starts and two substitute
      appearances?

EXPERT TRIVIA

791.　Which former Morton player once said of Rino Gattuso: 'He's like a tyrannosaurus rex with haemorrhoids!'

792.　In 1977, Morton had a run of 27 League matches without defeat. How many of the 27 did Morton win?

793.　Can you name the player signed from junior football in 1967 who, in his second and final match for Morton, scored a hat-trick in a 6-1 victory over Hamilton Accies?

794.　Can you name the Port Glasgow born midfielder who played for Morton from 1969 to 1971 and later won two caps for the USA?

795.　Which Morton player scored in two successive cup semi-finals in the 1960s?

796.　Which Morton player won the Third Division Players' Player of the Year Award in 2003?

797.　Can you name the classic television sitcom and the character who said: "When I'm out there I'm playing for Morton. Against Celtic at Hampden. And we stuff them'?

798.　Which two players were ever present in Morton's Second Division championship side of 2006/07?

799.　How many managers have Morton had (excluding caretakers) since 2000?

800.　Following on from the previous question, how many can you name?

ANSWERS

DAVIE IRONS

1.   *February*
2.   *Stirling Albion*
3.   *Eighth (2007/2008 season)*
4.   *Annan Athletic*
5.   *Gretna*
6.   *John*
7.   *False: He never won any international caps*
8.   *Hibernian*
9.   *1961*
10.   *Dunfermline Athletic*

LEGEND - ANDY RITCHIE

11.   *1956*
12.   *1976 (October)*
13.   *Clydebank*
14.   *St Mirren in a 5-1 defeat at Love Street*
15.   *22*
16.   *1979*
17.   *Peter Bonetti (a 4-1 victory against Dundee United)*
18.   *True*
19.   *Motherwell in 1983*
20.   *Jock Wallace*

MORTON AND ST. MIRREN - 1

21.   *1882*
22.   *True: During the 1900/1901 season*
23.   *David McGurn*
24.   *False: Drew one and lost three*
25.   *Kevin Thomas*
26.   *Keith Wright*
27.   *John Morrow and Harry Curran*
28.   *False: They met on League business in 1950/51 and 1951/52*
29.   *Scott McArthur*
30.   *Michael Hart*

THE EARLY YEARS

31.   *1874*

32.   Robert Fleming (v Ireland 1886)

33.   Garvel Park

34.   1893

35.   1893

36.   1879

37.   Harry Rennie in the 1890s

38.   Rangers. Morton lost 7-2.

39.   1900

40.   Rangers (Morton lost 3-0)

MORTON AND KILMARNOCK

41.   Third round

42.   Chris Templeman

43.   Kilmarnock: They won 3-2 at Cappielow and 5-1 at home

44.   2-1 to Morton

45.   True

46.   Morton: They finished fifth and Kilmarnock finished 13th

47.   Morton won 9-2

48.   Rugby Park

49.   True: Morton won two and drew two

50.   Alan Mahood

MORTON MANAGERS

51.   Kilmarnock

52.   1974

53.   Benny Rooney against Rangers in 1981 Scottish Cup

54.   Joe Gilroy in 1975

55.   Dave McPherson in 2002

56.   Motherwell in 1991

57.   Eddie Morrison

58.   Billy Stark

59.   Allan Evans with Aston Villa in 1982

60.   Jimmy Davies

LEAGUE GOALSCORERS - 1

61.   Mark McGhee   37

62.   Joe Caven   19

63.   Derek McInnes   19

64.	Jim Tolmie	17
65.	Marko Rajamaki	29
66.	John Goldthorp	36
67.	Dougie Robertson	50
68.	Jim Duffy	3
69.	John Boyd	4
70.	Hugh Strachan	4

LEGEND - ALLAN MCGRAW

71.	Glasgow
72.	1961
73.	58
74.	Ronnie Simpson
75.	Five
76.	Kilmarnock in a 5-1 victory
77.	1966
78.	1985
79.	1986/87
80.	Jackie McNamara

JIM McINALLY

81.	1964
82.	True
83.	Coventry City and Nottingham Forest
84.	10
85.	Four
86.	Celtic
87.	2004
88.	John McCormack
89.	Sligo Rovers
90.	Clyde

TON GOALIES

91.	David Harvey
92.	Denis Connaghan
93.	Bobby Russell
94.	Murray McDermott
95.	Jock Bradford who won a Scottish League Cap as a Morton

player in 1912

96. **Jim Herriot**
97. **Leif Nielsen**
98. **Dundee**
99. **Rab MacFarlane in 1896 against Wales**
100. **English**

LEAGUE APPEARANCES

101.	Jimmy Cowan	141
102.	Kai Johansen	35
103.	Bobby Adamson	26
104.	Murray McDermott	67
105.	Stan Seymour	233
106.	Jim Kiernan	194
107.	Barry Mitchell	3
108.	Chris Millar	179
109.	Jorn Sorenson	23
110.	Billy Sweeney	5

LEGEND – JOE HARPER

111. **1948**
112. **16 (against Partick Thistle)**
113. **The Summer Cup**
114. **29**
115. **Huddersfield Town**
116. **£35,000**
117. **Partick Thistle**
118. **1969**
119. **True: As a substitute against Iran**
120. **Hibernian**

LOAN PLAYERS

121. **Birmingham City**
122. **Hearts**
123. **Hibernian**
124. **Newcastle United**
125. **Dundee United**
126. **St Johnstone**

127.   *Dundee United*

128.   *Newcastle United*

129.   *Brighton and Hove Albion*

130.   *Newcastle United*

BENNY'S BOYS

131.   *Tommy Veitch*

132.   *Jimmy Miller*

133.   *Jim Tolmie*

134.   *Bobby Russell*

135.   *Bobby Thomson*

136.   *Jim Liddell*

137.   *Jim Rooney*

138.   *Roddie Hutchison*

139.   *John Hotson*

140.   *Eamon Lynch*

2008/2009

141.   *Jon Newby in a 1-1 draw against Clyde*

142.   *Allan McManus and Kevin Cuthbert*

143.   *True: Drew four and lost five*

144.   *Brian Wake*

145.   *Peter Weatherson*

146.   *6th*

147.   *Brian Wake*

148.   *Peter Weatherson*

149.   *True*

150.   *James Grady*

GREAT DANES

151.   *Bjarne Jensen*

152.   *Erik Sorensen*

153.   *Carl Bertlesen*

154.   *Preben Arentoft*

155.   *John Madsen*

156.   *Leif Nielsen from Houston Stars*

157.   *Flemming Nielsen from Atalanta*

158.   *Per Bartram*

159.   *Jorn Sorensen from Metz*

160.   *Kai Johansen (for Rangers in 1966)*

STRIKERS

161.   **Alex Mathie**

162.   **Peter Duffield**

163.   **Pat Ferry**

164.   **Kevin Hegarty**

165.   **Hugh McIlmoyle**

166.   **George French**

167.   **Davie Cupples**

168.   **Alec Linwood**

169.   **Joe Mason**

170.   **Bob Gibson (transferred to Dumbarton)**

1910-1919

171.   **Rangers 1 Morton 5**

172.   **James Stark and John May**

173.   **Stan Seymour**

174.   **Newcastle United in 1919**

175.   **Everton in 1913**

176.   **Port Glasgow Athletic**

177.   **The 1914/15 War Shield**

178.   **Second**

179.   **Morton 9 Hibernian 2**

180.   **Alex McNab**

WINNING GOALS

181.   **Billy McLaren**

182.   **Jim Tolmie**

183.   **Bobby Thomson**

184.   **Andy Ritchie**

185.   **Don Gillies**

186.   **Bobby Adamson**

187.   **John Murray**

188.   **Jim Rooney**

189.   **Bobby Russell**

190.   **John Goldthorp**

TON TRIVIA

191.   Tommy Gemmell (ex Celtic and Scotland)

192.   Stanley Matthews and Tommy Lawton

193.   Eric Liddell

194.   Finnbar Flood (1960s' goalkeeper)

195.   One (against Partick Thistle 1970)

196.   A bugle (the famous Cappielow Bugler)

197.   Jimmy Whyte (son Jim played for Aberdeen against Celtic in the 1967 Scottish Cup Final)

198.   Joe Gilroy when he was a player with Clyde

199.   Hugh Strachan

200.   Malcolm MacDonald (Newcastle United)

POSTIONS THEY PLAYED

201.   Full back

202.   Goalkeeper

203.   Centre half

204.   Right winger

205.   Goalkeeper

206.   Outside Left

207.   Right back

208.   Goalkeeper

209.   Goalkeeper

210.   Midfield

LEGEND – DEREK COLLINS

211.   1987

212.   Premier League

213.   Motherwell

214.   Rangers (in a 3-2 victory in 1988)

215.   Alex McLeish in 1998

216.   Partick Thistle

217.   Malta

218.   2001

219.   11

220.   St Johnstone

WHERE DID THEY COME FROM?

221. Hibernian
222. Queen of the South
223. Aarhus (Denmark)
224. Motherwell
225. Raith Rovers
226. Bronshoj (Denmark)
227. Partick Thistle
228. Partick Thistle
229. Bristol City
230. Ardeer Thistle

NICKNAMES

231. Jim Rooney
232. Hughie Smith (1930s)
233. Per Bartram and Joe Harper
234. John Goldthorp
235. Billy Osborne
236. Neil Mochan
237. Warren Hawke
238. Bobby Houston
239. Bobby Collins
240. Jimmy Wilson

DIVISION TWO CHAMPIONS - 2006/2007

241. Stirling Albion
242. 24
243. Peter Weatherson
244. 76
245. St Johnstone
246. Paul McGowan
247. Forfar Athletic
248. Four
249. Raith Rovers
250. True: Won nine and drew two

HAL'S HEROES

251. Bobby Adamson

252. Hibernian
253. Allan McGraw
254. John Boyd
255. Motherwell. Hugh Strachan, Morris Stevenson, Bobby Campbell and Jimmy Wilson
256. Joe Caven
257. 105,000 (actual figure 105,907)
258. Newcastle United in 1962
259. Partick Thistle in 1971
260. 'Keep rootin' folks!'

BIG WINS - 1

261. Tom Gracie and William Lindsay
262. Barney Jensen
263. Cove Rangers
264. Warren Hawke
265. East Fife
266. Morton 8 Brechin 0
267. Eight (5 in the 7-3 match and 3 in the 8-0 match)
268. Stewart Greacen and John Masaino
269. Gert Christensen
270. Billy Osborne

1920s

271. 1922
272. Alex McNab
273. 1922 (during and after a League match against Celtic)
274. First round against Raith Rovers
275. Charles Faultless, a goalkeeper with Morton who later became a referee
276. Semi-final (they lost to Kilmarnock)
277. Robert Cochran
278. Alec Leslie (Birmingham)
279. Jock Buchanan in 1929 when playing for Rangers
280. Jock McIntyre

TON TRIVIA 2

281. George Anderson

282. **Eddie Morrison**

283. **Three times**

284. **1992 for Sunderland against Liverpool**

285. **Queen of the South 6 Morton 5**

286. **Colin Stewart**

287. **Celtic**

288. **Drew Busby (against Dumbarton in 1967)**

289. **Marco Maisano**

290. **Don Gillies**

HISTORY

291. **11-0 v Carfin Shamrock in 1886**

292. **1-10 v Port Glasgow Athletic in 1894 and 1-10 v St Bernards 1933**

293. **265,258**

294. **Chelsea in the Inter-Cities Fairs Cup**

295. **Borge Thorup**

296. **The club reverted back to their traditional blue and white hoops for the first time since the 1950s.**

297. **Seven**

298. **Sixth in 1979/80**

299. **23,500 v Celtic 1922**

300. **It was the first time Scottish matches had been played on a Sunday**

POSITIONS IN THE LEAGUE - 1

301.	1989/1990	11th
302.	1988/1989	5th
303.	1987/1988	12th
304.	1986/1987	1st
305.	1985/1986	7th
306.	1984/1985	10th
307.	1983/1984	1st
308.	1982/1983	9th
309.	1981/1982	7th
310.	1980/1981	8th

MORTON AND ST MIRREN - 2

311.	1999/2000 in the First Division
312.	Morton 1 St Mirren 2 in 1978
313.	Erik Sorensen
314.	Morton 3 St Mirren 6
315.	Morton used three goalkeepers. Goalie Jim Liddell was red carded, and replaced by Jim Townsend and then Barry Evans
316.	Lex Richardson
317.	Bobby Adamson, Bobby Campbell and Jim Kiernan
318.	Paul Fenwick
319.	6-1 in season 1946/47
320.	True

BENNY'S BOYS - 2

321.	Jim Holmes
322.	1970 against Celtic
323.	Rangers in 1979 in a 2-2 draw at Ibrox
324.	Chelsea
325.	Davie Hayes
326.	Mike Jackson
327.	£25,000
328.	KSC Lokeren
329.	Bobby Thomson
330.	St Johnstone

NATIONALITIES - 1

331.	Robert Earnshaw	Welsh
332.	Dave Brcic	American
333.	John Maisano	Australian
334.	Martin Naylor	English
335.	Andre Boe	Cameroonian
336.	Karim Boukraa	French
337.	Finbarr Flood	Irish
338.	Kenneth Skovdam	Danish
339.	Marcus Sukalia	Austrian
340.	Mel Bottiglieri	Canadian

WHO AM I? - 1

341.   Denis Laughton

342.   Stan Rankin

343.   Craig McPherson

344.   John Hillcoat

345.   Jim Fleeting (father of Julie)

346.   Tom McNeil

347.   Danny Docherty

348.   Martin Doak

349.   Johnny Crum

350.   Jackie Wright

SCOTTISH CUP - 1922

351.   Aberdeen

352.   Morton 3 Aberdeen 1

353.   George French

354.   Jock Buchanan

355.   75,000

356.   Rangers

357.   Jimmy Gourlay

358.   It was the first time a goal had been scored in a Scottish Cup Final direct from a free kick.

359.   David Edwards

360.   Robert (Bob) McGregor

MORTON LEGENDS

361.   9

362.   1964

363.   Brentford in 1986

364.   George Anderson

365.   16

366.   Five

367.   False: He played six League Cup matches in 1976

368.   Falkirk

369.   Seven

370.   Dundee

CAPPIELOW CRACKERS

371. Carl Bertlesen
372. Mark McGhee
373. Morton 5 Hearts 3
374. Airdrie (3-1)
375. Davie Hayes, John Goldthorp, Andy Ritchie
376. Morton 3 Aberdeen 7 (after extra time)
377. Four
378. Alex Reid
379. Jim Tolmie
380. Ally Scott

2005/2006

381. Jim McInally
382. Second
383. 21
384. Derek Lilley
385. David McGurn
386. Scott McLaughlin
387. Peterhead
388. Raith Rovers
389. True: Won two and drew two
390. Alloa Athletic

TON TRANSFERS

391. John Clark and Steve Chalmers
392. £150,000
393. Preben Arentoft
394. £100,000
395. £500,000 from Leeds for Derek Lilley
396. £250,000 to MyPa-47 for Janne Lindberg and Marko Rajamaki
397. West Ham
398. Jim Duffy
399. Hugh McIlmoyle
400. Tottenham Hotspur

WHERE DID THEY GO?

401. Luton Town

402. Stenhousemuir
403. Airdrie
404. Livingston
405. Hamilton Accies
406. Stenhousemuir
407. Hamilton Accies
408. Raith Rovers
409. Dumbarton
410. Stranraer

LEGEND – BILLY STEEL

411. Denny in Stirlingshire
412. 1923
413. St Mirren
414. England in 1947
415. Three
416. Billy represented a Great Britain eleven against the rest of Europe
417. It was a British record
418. True
419. Dundee
420. 30

JOHN McNEIL

421. Cowal Boys Club
422. Peanuts
423. 16
424. Arbroath in 1976
425. Aberdeen
426. Dundee United
427. 79
428. Rangers
429. Dave Brcic
430. 16

1930s

431. Dan McRorie
432. Raith Rovers

433.	John Calder
434.	Matt Maley
435.	Bill Shankley (brother John played for Morton)
436.	David Torrance
437.	Alex Wilson in 1936
438.	1937
439.	117
440.	53

MATCH THE YEAR - 1

441.	1969
442.	1976
443.	1964
444.	1970
445.	1994
446.	1997
447.	1961
448.	1977
449.	1987
450.	1989

NAME THE YEAR

451.	1965 – Jorn Sorensen and Kai Johansen
452.	1968
453.	1977
454.	1985
455.	1967 (to Celtic)
456.	1952
457.	1964
458.	1979
459.	1970
460.	1992

NATIONALITIES - 2

461.	Stan Seymour	English
462.	Artur Correia	Angolan
463.	Paul Fenwick	Canadian
464.	Parfait Medou-Otye	French

465.	Jani Uotinen	Finnish
466.	Paddy Turner	Irish
467.	Martin Foster	English
468.	Lars Christensen	Danish
469.	Erik Paartalu	Australian
470.	Sean O'Connor	English

1940s

471. The Southern League Cup Final
472. St Mirren Park (Love Street)
473. Rangers
474. Jimmy Whyte
475. Celtic
476. Eddie Murphy
477. He was doing his National Service
478. Davie Cupples in a 3-0 victory
479. Johnny Kelly and Barnsley
480. 'Banana'

MORTON AND PARTICK THISTLE

481. 2-0 to Morton
482. Peter Weatherson
483. Brian Reid
484. Six: Four League matches and two League Cup matches
485. Five times
486. 7-1 (to Morton)
487. True: Two wins and two draws
488. Morton: They were formed in 1874, Partick Thistle were formed in 1876
489. Firhill Stadium
490. Derek Lilley

CAPPIELOW CAPTAINS

491. Jimmy Whyte
492. Billy Gray
493. Gerry Sweeney
494. Jim Kennedy
495. Jim Reilly

496.	Jim Holmes
497.	Davie Hayes
498.	Derek McInnes
499.	Derek Collins
500.	Bobby Thomson

POSITIONS IN THE LEAGUE - 2

501.	1999/2000	8th
502.	1998/1999	6th
503.	1997/1998	5th
504.	1996/1997	8th
505.	1995/1996	3rd
506.	1994/1995	1st
507.	1993/1994	11th
508.	1992/1993	6th
509.	1991/1992	7th
510.	1990/1991	9th

STRANGE BUT TRUE

511.	Tom Sinclair in the 1900s
512.	George McNeil
513.	Hugh Curran (scored for Scotland v England 1971 Home International)
514.	Crystal Palace – John Loughlan, Tony Taylor, Borge Thorup, Per Bartram
515.	Colin Jackson
516.	Jimmy Hill
517.	Donald Ford for Hearts
518.	Bernie Slaven in 1990
519.	Doug Cowie, Archie Robertson and Bobby Evans
520.	Eddie McIlvenny

ROY BAINES

521.	Derby
522.	1950
523.	Hibernian
524.	1976
525.	332

526.   Erik Sorensen

527.   Roy was injured and carried off on a stretcher and Morton lost 5-1

528.   182

529.   1979

530.   St Johnstone

LEGEND – JIMMY COWAN

531.   1926

532.   2007

533.   1944

534.   Hibernian in 1947

535.   Belgium in 1948

536.   1949

537.   25

538.   Bobby Collins

539.   Twice (1949 and 1951)

540.   Third Lanark

JIM HUNTER

541.   1964

542.   Glentyan Thistle

543.   Alloa Athletic

544.   1985

545.   43

546.   John Boag

547.   1996/97

548.   247 (plus six as substitute)

549.   One

550.   Brian Clough

1950s

551.   Bobby Collins (for Celtic against Aberdeen)

552.   Jimmy Mitchell

553.   Middlesborough

554.   £14,000

555.   Bert Gourlay (nephew of Jimmy)

556.   Jimmy Frizzell

557. *Three*

558. *12*

559. *Eddie Beaton*

560. *Johnny Hannigan*

AWAY GAMES

561. *Dumbarton*

562. *Stenhousemuir*

563. *Stranraer*

564. *Arbroath*

565. *Elgin City*

566. *Cowdenbeath*

567. *Annan Athletic*

568. *Montrose*

569. *Ross County*

570. *Forfar Athletic*

LEGEND – BILLY CAMPBELL

571. *1920*

572. *Morton Juniors*

573. *1941*

574. *England 8 Scotland 0*

575. *Bowie*

576. *Five*

577. *Jimmy Cowan*

578. *Billy burst his only pair of boots*

579. *1949*

580. *Ibrox Park*

2004/2005

581. *John McCormack*

582. *Third*

583. *Brechin City*

584. *Chris Millar and Peter Weatherson*

585. *Jim McAlister (started 35 matches and appeared once as a substitute)*

586. *Alloa Athletic*

587. *John Maisano*

588. *Livingston (2-1 at Almondvale)*

589. *Ryan Harding*

590. *18*

LEGEND – TOMMY ORR

591. *1924*

592. *16*

593. *Burma*

594. *Morton Juniors*

595. *Two*

596. *One*

597. *1958*

598. *107*

599. *1975 against Airdrie*

600. *Hibs, St Mirren and Queen of the South*

BIG WINS - 2

601. *Gerry Sweeney and Ian Campbell*

602. *Bobby Russell*

603. *St Mirren 1 Morton 4*

604. *Peter Weatherson 4, Jamie Stevenson 2, Bobby Linn, Chris Millar and Chris Templeman*

605. *Morton 9 Stenhousemuir 1*

606. *Jack Bolton*

607. *Barney Jensen*

608. *Clydebank*

609. *Morton 8 Cowdenbeath 4*

610. *Dougie Robertson*

1960s

611. *19th (last)*

612. *Doug Cowie*

613. *135*

614. *Tommy Docherty*

615. *True (Martin Ferguson)*

616. *Gordon Smith*

617. *Hearts – semi final replay*

618. *100*

619.   Sixth

620.   Terry Venables (for Chelsea)

DEREK LILLEY

621.   1974

622.   Everton Boys Club

623.   Three

624.   Dundee

625.   45

626.   George Graham

627.   Hearts

628.   85

629.   Livingston in 2004

630.   Forfar Athletic

1970s

631.   Jim Townsend

632.   Peter Bonetti

633.   Kenneth Skovdam

634.   1976

635.   Glencoe

636.   Nobby Stiles

637.   40 (in 1971)

638.   Ricky Sharp (brother of Graeme Sharp)

639.   Leningrad Zenit (Morton won 3-2)

640.   Steve Chalmers

2003/2004

641.   John McCormack

642.   Fourth

643.   Peter Weatherson and Alex Williams

644.   Airdrie United

645.   Arbroath

646.   Peter Weatherson

647.   True

648.   Alloa Athletic

649.   Alex Williams

650.   False: Won three, drew two and lost one

LEGEND - DAVID WYLIE

651.   *Ferguslie United*
652.   *Forfar in 1985*
653.   *The Cat*
654.   *482*
655.   *536*
656.   *Rangers*
657.   *Davie Irons*
658.   *Clyde in 1998*
659.   *14*
660.   *Airdrie in 1998*

JOE MASON

661.   *1940*
662.   *Kilmarnock*
663.   *First Division Championship with Kilmarnock*
664.   *Craig Watson*
665.   *Perry (after the television programme Perry Mason)*
666.   *Two*
667.   *43*
668.   *Four*
669.   *1972*
670.   *£10,000*

1980s

671.   *Martin Doak*
672.   *Aberdeen in 1980*
673.   *Alex Miller in 1983*
674.   *Willie Pettigrew*
675.   *Dougie Robertson (son David Robertson)*
676.   *Three times*
677.   *17*
678.   *John McNeil with 17 goals*
679.   *Roy Baines and Joe McLaughlin*
680.   *Allan Evans*

DIVISION THREE CHAMPIONS - 2002/2003

681.   *East Fife*

682. *21*

683. *Scott Bannerman*

684. *David Hopkin*

685. *Stirling Albion*

686. *True*

687. *Gretna*

688. *Alex Williams*

689. *Eddie Annand*

690. *David MacGregor*

EXPERT - HISTORY

691. *Celtic (2-0)*

692. *51*

693. *Huddersfield Town in 1971*

694. *1902 Scotland v Wales*

695. *1931*

696. *70*

697. *East Fife*

698. *West Bromich Albion in 1970*

699. *Neil Orr*

700. *Eric Smith, Tommy McLean, Allan Evans, Peter Cormack, Dave McPherson, Jim McInally*

DEBUTS

701. *Joe McLaughlin in 1978 against Partick Thistle*

702. *Billy Osborne*

703. *Joe Jordan*

704. *Dundee United in 1988*

705. *Montrose 2003*

706. *Peterhead 2002*

707. *Charlie Brown*

708. *Neil McNab*

709. *Morton 5 Partick Thistle 0*

710. *Stranraer in the Scottish League Cup in 2008*

EXPERT - ANDY RITCHIE

711. *128*

712. *The Irish League in 1980*

713.   *Neil Orr*

714.   *One*

715.   *John Goldthorp*

716.   *Sinclair Street End*

717.   *Albion Rovers*

718.   *St Mirren*

719.   *Twice*

720.   *58*

2001/2002

721.   *Peter Cormack*

722.   *Craig Coyle*

723.   *Warren Hawke*

724.   *Stenhousemuir*

725.   *Seven*

726.   *Sean O'Connor*

727.   *Phil Cannie*

728.   *Scott Bannerman*

729.   *10th*

730.   *Dave McPherson*

1990s

731.   *Three times – 1992, 1998, and 1999*

732.   *David Hopkin*

733.   *Two goals against Airdrie in 1995*

734.   *Peter Cormack*

735.   *John Anderson*

736.   *Queen of the South*

737.   *John Anderson*

738.   *1994/95*

739.   *64*

740.   *Derek McInnes*

MORTON AND THE 'OLD FIRM'

741.   *Bobby McKay and Jock Buchanan*

742.   *Craig Watson*

743.   *Twice*

744.   *Three times*

745.   John Murray
746.   Jim Gillespie
747.   Erik Sorensen, Jorn Sorensen, and Kaj Johansen
748.   Per Bartram (3) and Joe Harper
749.   Jim Tolmie
750.   Tommy Turner, Derek Collins and Rowan Alexander

EXPERT - JOE HARPER

751.   True: 1974 Scottish League Cup Final
752.   Hibernian
753.   Seven
754.   Peterhead
755.   £40,000
756.   Denmark (1972)
757.   Tommy Docherty
758.   Four
759.   Two
760.   Gerry Sweeney

2000/2001

761.   Alloa Athletic
762.   Ally Maxwell
763.   Ninth
764.   Stephen Whalen
765.   Kevin James
766.   True: Against Ayr United
767.   Ross Matheson
768.   Alloa Athletic
769.   Scott Paterson
770.   Nine

EXPERT - ALLAN MCGRAW

771.   Linfield
772.   The Variety Club of Great Britain
773.   Rowan Alexander
774.   Six
775.   1989
776.   12

777. John McMaster
778. 1994
779. Joe Caven with 22 goals
780. 16

2007/2008

781. Eighth
782. Nine
783. Clyde
784. Brian Wake, Ryan Harding and Kevin Finlayson
785. Stirling Albion
786. Jim McAlister
787. Four
788. Michael Gardyne
789. Iain Russell
790. Peter Weatherson

EXPERT TRIVIA

791. Ray Hudson in his capacity as a football commentator in the USA
792. 22
793. Jim McIntyre
794. George O'Neill
795. Willie Allan (against Hearts 1968, and Celtic 1969)
796. Alex Williams
797. Porridge, the character was McLaren
798. Ryan Harding and Jim McAlister
799. Nine
800. Billy Stark, Ian McCall, Allan Evans, Ally Maxwell, Peter Cormack, Dave McPherson, John McCormack, Jim McInally, Davie Irons

NOTES

NOTES

NOTES

NOTES

NOTES

OTHER BOOKS BY CHRIS COWLIN:

* Celebrities' Favourite Football Teams

* The British TV Sitcom Quiz Book

* The Cricket Quiz Book

* The Gooners Quiz Book

* The Official Aston Villa Quiz Book

* The Official Birmingham City Quiz Book

* The Official Brentford Quiz Book

* The Official Bristol Rovers Quiz Book

* The Official Burnley Quiz Book

* The Official Bury Quiz Book

* The Official Carlisle United Quiz Book

* The Official Carry On Quiz Book

* The Official Chesterfield Football Club Quiz Book

* The Official Colchester United Quiz Book

* The Official Coventry City Quiz Book

* The Official Doncaster Rovers Quiz Book

* The Official Heart of Midlothian Quiz Book

* The Official Hereford United Quiz Book

* The Official Hull City Quiz Book

* The Official Leicester City Quiz Book

OTHER BOOKS BY CHRIS COWLIN:

* The Official Macclesfield Town Quiz Book

* The Official Norwich City Football Club Quiz

* The Official Notts County Quiz Book

* The Official Peterborough United Quiz Book

* The Official Port Vale Quiz Book

* The Official Rochdale AFC Quiz Book

* The Official Rotherham United Quiz Book

* The Official Shrewsbury Town Quiz Book

* The Official Stockport County Quiz Book

* The Official Sunderland Quiz Book

* The Official Watford Football Club Quiz Book

* The Official West Bromwich Albion Quiz Book

* The Official Wolves Quiz Book

* The Official Yeovil Town Quiz Book

* The Reality Television Quiz Book

* The Southend United Quiz Book

* The Ultimate Derby County Quiz Book

* The Ultimate Horror Film Quiz Book

* The West Ham United Quiz Book

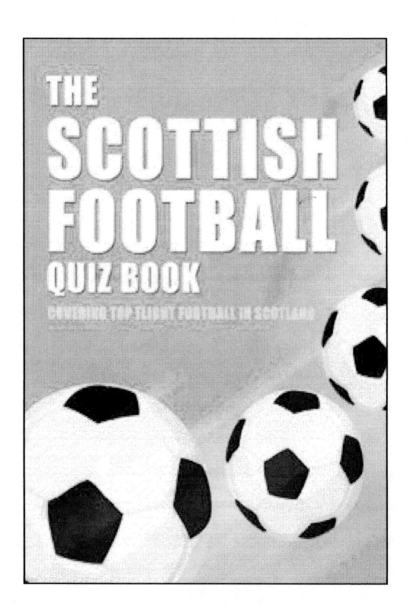

ALSO BY GRAEME ROSS:

The Scottish Football Quiz Book

Covering Top Flight Football in Scotland

Forewords by John Wark and Alex McLeish
£9.99 (Hardback)

About the book:
Are you an aficionado of the Scottish Football League? Are you up-to-date with all the latest fixtures and club news? Looking for an opportunity to test and extend your knowledge? Then this quiz book is just what you have been waiting for. Containing 1,000 challenging questions The Scottish Football Quiz Book has been designed to put Scottish football fans through their paces.

There are sections covering all aspects of the game including players, managers, scores, transfers, opponents, wins, losses and draws as well as all the memorable matches that have shaped the Scottish Football League down the years.

This book is as informative as it is entertaining and is guaranteed to provide hours of fun for football enthusiasts of all ages. You'll be crying foul and calling for extra time as you strive to recall all the people and places that have played an important part in the history of Scottish football.

This fitting tribute is a must have for all Scottish football fans and anyone interested in learning more about the beautiful game north of the border.

www.apexpublishing.co.uk